In Praise of *From Loss ... to Li*

"Who knew some of our biggest heartaches would be our greatest teachers? Beth Bolthouse did. She gently guides you through the sacred and scary parts of life, your grief. She knows there are riches and growth beyond it. She takes you along the journey of self-understanding to find peace, self-compassion, and perspective. Her expertise and empathy are manifest as she explains the evidence-based research of posttraumatic growth. But it is her voice and gentle guidance you hear as you exercise through this workbook."

   —Kathey Batey, Divorce Support Anonymous, Author of the Suddenly Single Series

"If you're ready for it, this workbook contains life-altering pages. It's easy to understand yet gives the tools and prompts to really transform how to respond to our ongoing grief and loss in tangible ways. It aids in creating a new lens for finding purpose in each day ahead."

   —Amy Geldersma, LMSW, Social Work and Counseling Services Manager, Harbor Hospice and Palliative Care

"This workbook not only helped me work through the trauma of losing my husband, but it also helped me look to the future and realize the goals I want to achieve. It has become a great resource to refer back to when the emotional waves of grief and loss come crashing back."

   —J.B.

"This workbook is an essential tool for grief. It really helped me integrate my emotions and move forward in life with hope for the future."

   —L.E.

"This workbook can help you look into a mirror full of grief and confusion and walk through it with the emotional and spiritual tools for a life of positive growth. Carefully crafted with love and insight to assist the grieving person in reviewing their spiritual, emotional, social, and physical lives, it takes you on a journey of hope and healing. I highly recommend it."

   —M.P.

"The focus of *From Loss ... to Life!* is positive growth. It contains exercises focusing on rebuilding one's self through reflection and practicing resilience. This is not a book for 'beginning grievers.' The techniques require one to look objectively at one's grieving self and develop the resolve to create a new self that can tolerate the painful task of making one's self anew. If taken to heart and applied, this material can help counterbalance grief with positive growth. It helped me to create a focus on resilience and positive actions, attitudes, and what I can do to go on living without my spouse."

   —W.J.

From Loss ...to Life!

Transform your life
after traumatic loss

Beth Bolthouse, MA, MS, LPC

SOUL SEASONS
PUBLISHING BY DESIGN

From Loss ... to Life! Transform your life after traumatic loss

© 2020 by Beth Bolthouse, MA, MS, LPC

Soul Seasons Publishing
P.O. Box 195
Lowell, Michigan 49331
www.soulseasonspublishing.com

Published 2020
Printed in the United States of America

ISBN 13: 978-1-7346859-4-7 (ebook)
ISBN 13: 978-1-7346859-3-0 (paperback)
Library of Congress Control Number: 2020919843

Library of Congress Cataloging-in-Publication Data

Name: Bolthouse, Beth, 1957 -
Title: From loss ... to life! Transform your life after traumatic loss / Beth Bolthouse
Description: Lowell, MI : Soul Seasons, 2020 | Includes bibliographical references.
Identifiers: LCCN 2020919843 | ISBN 9781734685947 (ebook) | ISBN 9781734685930
        (paperback)
Subjects: PSYCHOLOGY/ General / Grief and Loss / Group Psychology / Mental Health
        SELF-HELP / Death, Grief, Bereavement / Posttraumatic Stress Disorder
        SOCIAL SCIENCE / Death and Dying / Thanatology

LC record available at https://lccn.loc.gov/2020919843

Downloadable files from this workbook are available at http://lifeinvestmentnetwork.wordpress.com.

Cover design: Beth Bolthouse
Cover image: "The road separating the desert and the oasis" by Ievgenii Tryfonov. Used by permission.
Interior design: Beth Bolthouse and Soul Seasons Publishing
Editing: Soul Seasons Publishing
Proofreading: Deborah Stenberg

Dedicated to every person who has courageously persevered

through their own journey of loss

CONTENTS

INTRODUCTION

I am a Licensed Professional Counselor, and in 2007, after working in private practice for several years I began serving hospice families as well as other people in our West Michigan communities who have been devastated by loss. This workbook was developed for those who are one year or more beyond their loss and desire to go deeper within their physical, social, emotional, and spiritual selves. While walking alongside many grieving people, I have heard stories of their experiences of going through hell and high water, and navigating the muck and mire of intense grief resulting from many and varied traumatic losses, including deaths, relationships, finances, faith, violence, and more. They've been to support groups, educational seminars, individual grief therapy, and have gone as far as they can go through those means. It has been exciting to format these pages with input from these folks who understand grief in ways that teach me, who willingly take risks of vulnerability to share with each other, and who provide the support needed to move through the process of posttraumatic growth. Throughout the process of posttraumatic growth, they have learned about their strengths and vulnerabilities, discovered ways to relate in a variety of relationships using healthy boundaries, and identified attachments that might have sabotaged them along the way. Most of all, they chose to be intentional in their thinking and actions. They are still grieving, yet they are also empowered and have found renewal for their lives, which they never thought possible.

The concepts and principles of posttraumatic growth result from evidence-based research led by Richard Tedeschi and Lawrence Calhoun. These men are the pioneers of the important process of moving forward through making positive changes to adapt to traumatic, stressful, life-changing events. These events include the death of a loved one, the loss of a job, a tragedy involving a family member or other close relationship, or any number of horrific, devastating wounds or losses one goes through in life. Tedeschi and Calhoun developed the Posttraumatic Growth Inventory, which has been validated by numerous research studies as an effective measure of posttraumatic growth following a traumatic loss. Readers who want to know more about their fine work are directed to the references list at the end of this workbook.

This workbook follows in Tedeschi & Calhoun's footsteps by utilizing counseling techniques in practical ways that help individuals and groups apply these tools, encouraging adaptation, transformation, and resilience, which are vital to healing. We will incorporate these five measures of the Posttraumatic Growth Inventory into the sections of this workbook: appreciation for life, relationship with self and others, personal strength, new possibilities, and spiritual development.

Tedeschi & Calhoun's work led to the development of *The Posttraumatic Growth Workbook* (Tedeschi & Moore, 2016). It is a step-by-step guide that helps readers to identify the lessons of trauma, establish new priorities, find meaning in what happened, and grow beyond the trauma experience to help others.

Another notable workbook is by Arielle Schwartz. In *The Post-Traumatic Growth Guidebook* (Schwartz, 2020), she focuses on finding ways to engage trauma recovery through yoga, EMDR, relational therapy, and other healing techniques.

This *From Loss… to Life!* workbook takes us into deeper self-exploration and helps us identify personal and practical ways to engage with ourselves and others in order to bring greater purpose and meaning out of our losses so we can live intentionally and with joy.

Thank you, Dave Beach and Soul Seasons Publishing; Deb Stenberg; Kathey Batey; Amy Geldersma, Laura Ecker, and the entire Harbor Hospice family; and each person who has allowed me to join them in their grief journeys. Most of all, my gratitude to God who grieves with us, walks alongside us, and whose own vulnerability and transparency of godly grief have perhaps given us the best example of posttraumatic growth.

Note: PDFs of each of the worksheets contained in this workbook are available free of charge at http://lifeinvestmentnetwork.wordpress.com.

§ § §

"The only lasting trauma is the one we suffer without positive change."
Leo Buscaglia

A New Chapter in Your Life

If your loss was over a year ago and you have participated in some form of grief counseling (groups or individual support or self-study), and you are ready to begin making positive changes in your life, this workbook is for you.

At least a year since your loss is specified not because it is the "magic timeframe" but rather because most people who have gone through a significant loss are ready to begin looking for increased purpose and meaning in their lives after their first year of grieving.

Posttraumatic Growth refers to the phenomenon of "positive psychological change experienced as a result of the struggle with highly challenging life circumstances" (Tedeschi & Calhoun, 2004, p. 1). This workbook is divided into six sections, which will guide you toward increasing a sense of purpose, growing in resilience, and formulating identity in meaningful ways so that, although losses will continue to occur in the future, you will be better equipped to manage them and make healthy choices in the long-term. Each of the six sections provides opportunities to apply post-traumatic growth principles to four areas of your life: emotional, social, physical, and spiritual. You are encouraged to utilize this material for individual self-study or in the context of a small group, which can provide meaningful support while working through the material.

It is hoped you will utilize this workbook to strategize with others who also would like to become more active in their lives and communities after going through a significant loss. Sharing your journey in a group or with others of like-mindedness can become even more empowering as you learn new goals, engage in activities, and find your resilience together.

Self-Assessment

To begin, let's identify where you are in the grieving continuum today. Please take a few moments to check only the boxes that apply. The point value of each item is provided. Information about scoring is provided on the next page.

	Description	Points
	Level 3	
	Shock	3
	Disbelief	3
	Numbness	3
	Difficulty Concentrating	3
	Rage	3
	Suicidal Thinking	3
	Focusing / Obsessing on my loss	3
	Total Level 3	
	Level 2	
	Realize I need to make changes in my life	2
	Believe there is life after my loss, and it can be meaningful	2
	Have participated in grief counseling or grief group of some type (including self-study)	2
	Experience grief symptoms less frequently and less intensely than when the loss first happened	2
	Feel ready to begin finding meaning and purpose in life	2
	Total Level 2	
	Level 1	
	Have more good days than bad	1
	Fully accept the finality of the loss (i.e., my loved one is dead)	1
	Have started doing work, volunteering, or hobbies that bring meaning to my life	1
	Feel more joy and peacefulness	1
	Feel I have begun reinvesting in my life	1
	Would like to know myself better	1
	Have a desire to redefine/identify my purpose without my loved one (or without what existed prior to my loss)	1
	Look forward to a future	1
	Total Level 1	

© Beth Bolthouse

After you have checked your choices, add up the total to provide a numerical assessment of your readiness to proceed with the workbook exercises.

Total Level 3: _____ If you have **more than 6 points**, you may not be ready to work through this material, and you are strongly encouraged to seek professional grief counseling.

Total Level 2: _____ If you have **less than 4 points**, you may not be ready to work through this material.

Total Level 1: _____ If you have **less than 2 points**, you may not be ready to work through this material.

If your score indicates you are not yet ready to move through the exercises in this workbook, set it aside and do this assessment exercise in six months.

If you find you have suicidal thinking, you are strongly encouraged to find an appropriate mental health professional. The National Suicide Lifeline is available 24/7; call 1-800-273-TALK (8255) or text 741741.

SECTION 1: GRIEF EXPLORED

Exploring My Story of Loss

Identify the ways your family of origin dealt with loss. Please describe emotions, behaviors, and communications that took place in your family (yourself or others in the family) during or after a loss of any kind (death, move, pet, other loss) when you were growing up:

Type of Loss	Emotions	Behaviors	Communications
Example: *Death of my cat*	*Sad, upset, angry*	*Crying, isolating*	*"Don't be upset; we can get another cat tomorrow."*

© Beth Bolthouse

Group: Invite participants to share the stories of their losses, the feelings they experienced, and ways their lives have been changed as a result of these losses.

Discuss or write about the loss you would like to work through as you use this workbook.

The Loss: _____

_____

_____

_____

Initial Reaction: _____

_____

_____

_____

Who supported you? _____

_____

_____

_____

What was the first year like for you? _____

_____

_____

_____

What helped you? _____

_____

_____

_____

What mistakes do you feel you made because of this loss? _____

_____

_____

_____

Levels of Loss

Using the tool provided on the next page (see sample below), complete the fill-in boxes to identify the levels of loss you have experienced since the event. Note that each section represents one of four areas of your life: physical, social, spiritual, and emotional.

- In the **center circle**, write the **date of your loss**.

- In each of the LEVEL 1 boxes, identify changes you experienced in the **first year** after your loss (physical, social, emotional, and spiritual changes).

- Then in each of the LEVEL 2 circles, write words or phrases that characterize ways you have personally changed in each of the four areas since your loss occurred.

- In each of the LEVEL 3 boxes, identify a specific growth opportunity in each of the four areas based on the changes you experienced and the ways you have personally changed as a result of your loss.

Note: These boxes will help you see options available to you for setting goals and choosing what you may want to focus on throughout the course of working through this workbook.

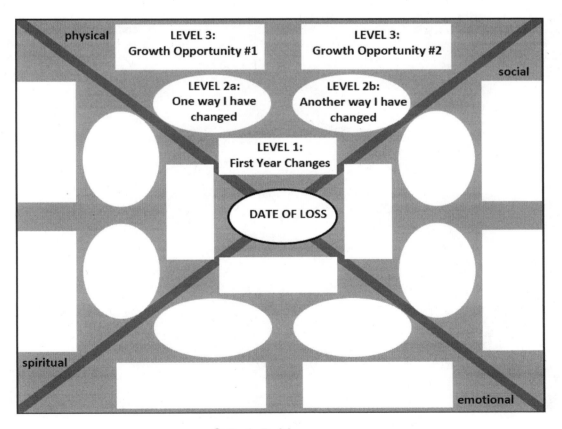

© Beth Bolthouse

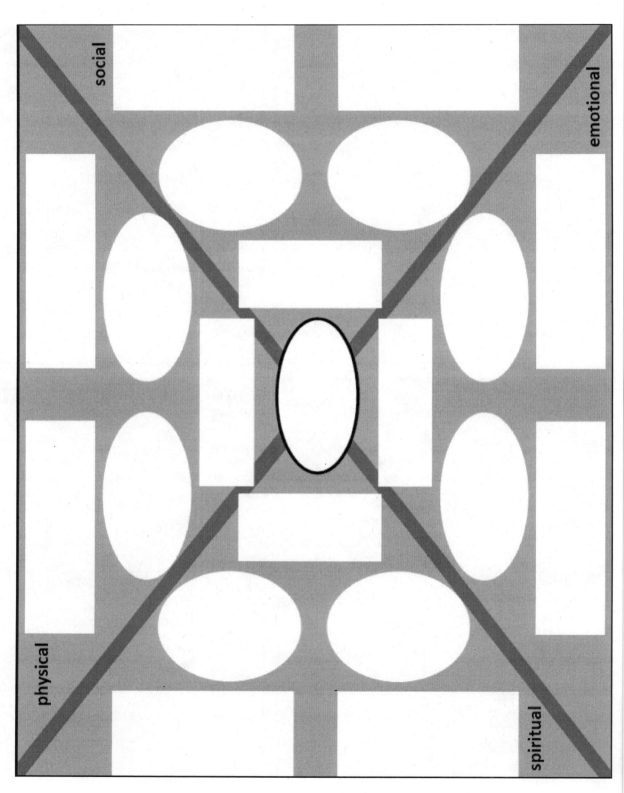

social

emotional

physical

spiritual

What is Grief?

There are many and varied emotions and thoughts relating to grief. Many grievers describe feeling like they are being jerked around by a roller coaster, never knowing when the next curve or drop will happen. Others relate grief to waves that come and go—ranging from mild ups and downs to what feels like a tsunami (and everything in between). It is okay and normal to feel sad, depressed, worried, numb, and any other feeling you are experiencing. Most people say they feel several feelings at once. Sometimes you may have tears; other times, the tears won't come. Grief can teach us, so it is important to be curious and notice what is happening when we grieve.

Thoughts of grief can include remembering who died or what happened, replaying events, having difficulty concentrating, short term memory loss, focusing on "what if's" and thinking about regrets.

Naming your thoughts and feelings has value in understanding them. In the space provided below, make a list of the feelings and thoughts you have experienced in your grief journey:

_____

_____

_____

_____

_____

_____

_____

_____

_____

_____

_____

_____

_____

_____

Understanding Traumatic Grief

William Worden (2009) defines "traumatic grief" as what occurs when someone experiences a death (or other loss), which results in trauma symptoms (p. 7).

When you compare and contrast traumatic grief with posttraumatic stress disorder (PTSD), it is important to note that symptoms may be similar. Read through the list on the next page and decide what you do and do not relate to. Many grievers who initially experience trauma symptoms find that those symptoms diminish over time as they work through their grief. Other grievers continue to struggle with traumatic symptoms, and their grief work includes learning new ways to manage trauma in addition to coping with grief.

Types of traumatic loss

Not all experiences of loss are the same for every person. Someone whose mother has died may feel at peace and even relieved as part of their grief, and not have stress with coping. Others grieving the loss of their mother may experience high anxiety, feelings of abandonment, sleep disruption, feel easily startled, replay scenes from the death over and over in their mind, etc. There are many factors involved in whether a loss is traumatic or not. It may or may not involve a death; it may be a very painful or traumatizing life event, such as an auto accident, unexpected job loss, being assaulted, experiencing betrayal, or experiencing several losses within a short time. Each person's life experience, personality, level of resilience, and attachment style factor into whether a loss is traumatic for him or her.

Symptoms of traumatic grief

Some research studies have suggested that many intense symptoms can indicate whether a loss is traumatic, including some relating to posttraumatic stress disorder. On the next page, you will find a partial list.

Symptoms of Traumatic Grief

Mark the box next to the one(s) you relate to or have experienced following your loss. If you have one or more of these, it is also important to note the level of intensity you experience.

Then identify how frequently you experience each item you checked using a scale of 1 to 10, where 1 is "rarely," and 10 is "all the time," and write the appropriate number on each line provided.

Check all that apply and rate 1 to 10 (1 = Rarely; 10 = All the time).

- ☐ Recurring thoughts and images about the loss _____
- ☐ Extreme loneliness _____
- ☐ Yearning, longing, or pining for the deceased _____
- ☐ Psychological or physical reactions (triggers) _____
- ☐ Sleep disturbance _____
- ☐ Significant reduction of interest or motivation to participate in life activities _____
- ☐ Feeling detached or isolating self from others _____
- ☐ Difficulty concentrating _____
- ☐ Intensified anxiety, fear, panic _____
- ☐ Feeling like part of yourself has died _____
- ☐ Feeling hopeless about the future _____
- ☐ Trust and/or security has been disrupted _____
- ☐ Sense of emptiness _____
- ☐ Feeling bitter _____
- ☐ Increasing physical ailments or illnesses _____

Based on the level of frequency for each of the symptoms you checked, you may be realizing your loss affected you more than you realized. The purpose of this workbook is not to diagnose you but rather to provide opportunities for greater insight into what you are experiencing, so you can better understand how you are thinking, feeling, and behaving, as well as offer options for coping differently.

Note: If at any time you are thinking about hurting yourself or someone else, please contact a mental health professional for additional support. If you are struggling with suicidal thoughts, the National Suicide Lifeline is available 24/7; call 1-800-273-TALK (8255) or text 741741.

Challenges with traumatic grief

Trauma can leave us feeling panicked, isolated, fearful. We may have nightmares, flashbacks, an inability to go to work, or lack of interest in day-to-day activities we used to enjoy before our loss. Grief can feel manageable one moment and overwhelming the next. People in our lives may wonder why the loss is affecting us so much. They may wonder after a year or more, why we don't just get over the grief. They will have ideas and advice that they think will get us back on track. Even though they may have good intentions, we can be left feeling shame for our grief and even more helpless and hopeless as a result of the expectations of others.

Acknowledging our feelings is an important component of dealing with traumatic grief. Rather than stuffing emotions inside or trying to ignore them (both of which will make trauma intensify), writing our feelings down in a journal or checking off a list of feelings each day can validate our emotional experience. The Appendix contains a feeling word list that can be used for this purpose.

Permitting yourself to be exactly where you are now is another essential piece of managing traumatic grief. Let go of expectations, and instead give yourself permission to do your best or wait until later to tackle a task. Refuse to let negative self-talk have a voice. When you hear those types of shaming statements or find yourself stressing over whether someone else is pleased with you, remind yourself that you have suffered a deep loss and are working on things as best as you can. Remember that you are not responsible for what someone else thinks, only for what you choose to do for yourself.

Secondary Losses

Recognizing "secondary losses"—those things that change or go away after the initial loss—is also an important component of acknowledging where we are in our loss journey.

Types of secondary losses

Often, we don't recognize that we are grieving additional things as well as the person or situation or the significant role they play in our grief journey. For example, when a spouse dies, the widow/er also may experience the loss of income, plans for retirement, the companionship they experienced, and the home they shared. Parents experience secondary losses when a baby dies—seeing them grow up, graduate from school, get married, have children, and other things that will no longer happen now that s/he is gone. Each loss, whether a person or a circumstance, can also have a domino effect of some kind.

Jill LaMorie (2013), in her article "Recognizing and Grieving Secondary Losses," relates these to the ripple effect created when one throws a stone into still water, creating a disturbance that causes circles of motion one after another (para. 1).

As we consider the "ripple effect" we have experienced after our initial loss, what are some of our other losses? Some examples include:

- Loss of security (including changes in income, housing, job/career, feelings of safety and confidence)

- Loss of relationships (including future plans, role in family, traditions, support system)

- Loss of individuality (including identity, purpose, faith, motivation, health)

Disenfranchised grief and loss

People often experience loss and grief that people are not recognized in their social circle or by society in general. Kenneth Doka (2002) identified disenfranchised loss using the following criteria:

- The relationship was not considered socially acceptable, important, or legitimate.

- The loss is not seen as significant.

- The griever is either not included in rituals relating to the loss (such as a memorial service or scattering of ashes) or viewed as someone who should not be or is unable to grieve the loss.

- Some parts of the loss are embarrassing or unacceptable; therefore, the griever is marginalized (examples: the death of a pet, grieving the death of a mistress, being fired from a job) (as cited in Harris & Winokuer, 2016, p. 49).

Identifying specific secondary losses and ways they have impacted me

Take a few moments to consider the secondary losses you have experienced (including any in which you feel marginalized or disenfranchised).

On the next page, make a list on the chart in each of the areas indicated (physical, social, emotional, spiritual) as to ways you have been affected. There is no right or wrong way to make this list—write your secondary losses wherever you think they belong.

Social

Physical

Secondary Losses

Emotional

Spiritual

Acknowledging My Strengths

Part of healing through grief involves getting to know ourselves in light of the loss(es) we have experienced. Many times, our identity is shaken; we begin to realize we have changed, and it can leave us feeling uncertain as to our identity. Part of growing through grief is identifying our strengths and realizing the positives we have within our personality.

Carl Jung (1971) developed a theory of psychological types that identify many of the strengths each person has within their personality. Take several minutes to complete the following exercise, designed to identify the positives about your personality, ways you function in the world, and how you think. If you are working through this material with a group, bring your results to the next session.

Go online to http://www.humanmetrics.com/cgi-win/jtypes2.asp and complete the "Jung Typology" questionnaire. Then fill in your results and any comments below:

My personality type is _____

What surprised you about these results? _____

_____

_____

_____

_____

_____

Was anything confirmed for you regarding your personality style? _____

_____

_____

_____

_____

_____

In reading the side-bar listings (communication style, learning style, etc.), do you agree or disagree, and why/why not? _____

_____

_____

_____

_____

_____

_____

What, if anything, in these results differ from how you saw yourself before your loss? _____

_____

_____

_____

_____

_____

Other comments? _____

_____

_____

_____

_____

_____

Goal Setting

What would you like to accomplish over the next six months?

Every January 1st, I think of something I would like to accomplish during the next 12 months. Sometimes it's a simple resolution, such as changing my attitude or getting more rest. When I have a bigger goal to accomplish, using a technique such as "S.M.A.R.T." helps me not only identify my goal but also break it down into more details that guide me, so it's more likely I will accomplish it.

S.M.A.R.T. is a formula to help people identify what they would like to accomplish and how they want to get there successfully. It was developed by George Doran (1981) and stands for Specific, Measurable, Attainable, Relevant, Time (pp. 35-36). Using the **S.M.A.R.T.** acronym, please complete the items on the following page. (An example is provided here if you are unsure how to respond to one or more questions).

1. **Specific goal:** Write one sentence describing something you would like to accomplish over the next 6 months.

   By the end of 6 months, I would like to go on a cruise just like my husband and I had planned to do before he died.

2. **Measurable:** Write a list of ways I will know I am meeting my goal.

   I will explore cruises, decide on a date, talk with friends about joining me, purchase tickets, go on the cruise.

3. **Attainable:** is this something that I can realistically accomplish in the next 6 months?
   Yes.

   What motivates you to accomplish this goal?

   It is something I've always wanted to do, yet when my husband died it seemed it would never happen. This will be a trip to look forward to and also feel good to fulfill something my husband also wanted to do.

4. **Relevant:** How does this goal have meaning and purpose to my life at the present time?

   It will provide motivation to work on becoming stronger in my grief, make plans for my future, and help me feel like I am living my life.

5. **Time-bound:** What date or timeframe will I plan to meet this goal?

   By the end of summer.

My S.M.A.R.T. Goal

Specific goal: Write one sentence describing something you would like to accomplish over the next 6 months.

By the end of 6 months, I would like to _____

_____

This is important to me because _____

_____

How will this make my life better? _____

_____

Measurable: Write a list of ways you will know you are meeting your goal. _____

_____

_____

Attainable: Can you realistically accomplish this goal in the next 6 months? _____

What motivates you to accomplish this goal? _____

_____

_____

Relevant: How does this goal have meaning and purpose in your life at the present time? _____

_____

_____

Time-bound: What date or timeframe will you plan to meet this goal? _____

_____

SECTION 2: APPRECIATION FOR LIFE

In this section, we are going to take a look at the things that weigh us down—the rubbish and remains of loss over the years of your life—and how to remove it from your life, prioritize the good things, and begin to value yourself and the changes you are making in your life.

This toxic waste may have accumulated over many years; some may have begun to pile up with the recent stress and trauma you have experienced. To open new doors to meaning and healthy relationships, we need to look at those things that have been sabotaging us. Just like a hoarder who has lived in filth and disorder a long time, we have gotten used to the clutter and trash we have been carrying around and perhaps even hanging onto. Sometimes this debris can have more negative power over us than the stress and traumas that began our hoard collection in the first place.

Take a few moments to reflect on the hurts you feel inside. Close your eyes, breathe slowly, and allow yourself to take an honest inward look. The hurts and wounds we experience can produce some pretty unhealthy thoughts, feelings, and behaviors.

Using the list on the next page, check off the items you can identify as part of who you have become or how you have lived regardless of the intensity level. Then go back to each item and note specific people or circumstances that have contributed to it.

Sifting Through Debris in Your Life

Check the items you identify with and note specific people and circumstances.

☐ Resentment _____

☐ Envy _____

☐ Pride _____

☐ Worry/anxiety _____

☐ Victim-thinking _____

☐ Jealousy _____

☐ Toxic people/relationships _____

☐ Not feeling purposeful or useful _____

☐ Fear _____

☐ Pressure from society/family/expectations _____

☐ Clutter and accumulated "stuff" _____

☐ Gossipers _____

☐ Other "baggage" _____

☐ Non-essential items _____

☐ Drama _____

☐ Chaos _____

☐ Misunderstandings _____

☐ Hate _____

☐ Self-doubt _____

☐ Pessimism _____

☐ Negativity _____

Each of the items listed above is a negative way most people adapt to loss. The helplessness and aloneness of trauma and stress put us into survival mode, and *we will use just about anything to help us feel some type of control so we can try to get back to normal!* The problem is *our feeble attempts don't work!* And we can find ourselves feeling worse and working even harder to either fake it or give up.

But we have also used positive coping skills. As significant as looking at the negative clutter and rubbish we have accumulated, it is just as important to affirm that we have done things well. And there are positive ways we have adapted to our loss.

Healthy Responses to Stress and Trauma

Using the list below, check off those you relate to and acknowledge these healthy responses to stress and trauma. Note specific people and circumstances for each item you identify.

☐ Set boundaries _____

☐ Reached out to someone safe for support _____

☐ Journaled my feelings and thoughts _____

☐ Took time for self-care _____

☐ Cried _____

☐ Said "No" without guilt _____

☐ Went to a support group _____

☐ Noticed the beauty of nature _____

☐ Connected with spirituality _____

☐ Expressed my grief through art or music _____

☐ Expressed kindness to another _____

☐ Took a mental health day _____

☐ Meditated or prayed _____

☐ Exercised _____

☐ Ate a delicious meal _____

☐ Expressed gratitude _____

☐ Took a nap _____

☐ Did something in honor or memory of my loved one _____

☐ Got up, got dressed, and accomplished something meaningful _____

Using the Feeling Words list provided in the Appendix, take a moment to write some of the emotions you are feeling now when you consider both the positive and negative ways you have responded and adapted to your loss: _____

_____

_____

_____

_____

_____

_____

_____

_____

Language Matters

Shame is also a part of loss. We do not have to have caused the loss to feel shame about an aspect of what happened, how we feel, the thoughts that go through our head, or the images that won't leave our mind. We tend to beat ourselves up for what we do or don't do instead of affirming the ways we have dealt with grief thus far.

So how can we identify language which empowers us instead of shames us in our grief? To begin, we can look at the 3 Cs of empowering language: Challenge, Courage, Confidence (Doka, 2018, p. 14).

Challenge beliefs

What are the things you used to believe about yourself, others, the world, even God or spirituality? Loss challenges the things we used to take for granted, sometimes disrupting what we thought was true about our life. We live our lives in a sense of comfort and security that we often take for granted. We experience stress at work but make it to 5 pm and feel both a sense of relief and accomplishment for surviving the day. Perhaps we put money aside for retirement, save for a vacation, or a down payment on a new vehicle. Yet, what happens to our beliefs about success, security, or the future if the next morning we go to work and receive a layoff notice effective immediately? Then after weeks of searching for a job, we are running out of unemployment, unable to make the house payment, feeling more alone and helpless to make ends meet, uncertain who to turn to, and wondering why God let this happen. This is one example of how a loss can become a stressful, even traumatic, situation that challenges our beliefs about ourselves, others, the world, and even our spirituality.

Below is an example of ways my beliefs were challenged when I suddenly lost a long-term job I had with a Christian ministry and discovered that unemployment was not available.

About …	Before my loss, I believed …	After my loss, I believed …
Myself	*I would never leave my job; I was fulfilled; I was successful*	*I am a failure; I am alone and helpless; I am worthless*
Others	*People are reliable and trustworthy; they care*	*I don't know who to trust; people betray you without warning*
The World	*The world is challenging, but I can deal with what comes my way*	*I am lost and without direction; it is hard to find employment*
God or Spirituality	*God loves me, cares for me, provides for me*	*God loves me, cares for me, provides for me, but also may allow terrible pain in my life*

Now, take a moment to reflect on what you believed *before* your loss and what you believe *now*—did anything change.

About …	Before my loss, I believed …	After my loss, I believe …
Myself		
Others		
The World		
God or Spirituality		

Stop for a moment, and reflect on what you wrote. Consider whether you have found any of your former beliefs challenging or whether there has been a shift or a change in your beliefs.

It is not wrong to challenge our beliefs. When we experience intense grief, we also question many of the things we used to take for granted or believed to be true. Our world is turned upside down. We are not the same person we were before the loss. We doubt what we used to trust. We sense more fear about what we used to feel confident about. It is important to identify the questions we have, our doubts and fears, which are a part of our life now.

What is something you question now that you did not question before your loss? _____

_____

_____

What is something you doubt now that you felt confident about before your loss? _____

_____

_____

What fears are you aware of now that used to be minimal or not an issue prior to your loss? _____

_____

_____

Recognizing these and acknowledging that they are a part of your grief is essential as you move into the next C—Courage.

Courage with self and others

How do we take the challenges of our beliefs and use them in a meaningful way so we can begin developing the courage to face the fears and challenges we are encountering? One answer is by considering the following three areas:

1. **Accept the consequences of the loss**

Accepting consequences is one of the most difficult things to do, yet one of the most important. Every loss has consequences which we resist facing and accepting. Some consequences are physical (for example, moving to a different home); some are social (people we thought would be there for us have detached or disappeared); some are financial (not having enough money to pay bills); some are spiritual (loss of faith or trust); some are mental and emotional (increased anxiety, lack of security or stability).

How has this loss affected you? What are the consequences you have experienced? _____

_____

_____

_____

2. **Make changes to boundaries with ourselves and others**

Sometimes loss gives us unwanted changes in our life; taking that power back by choosing the changes we would like to make can be a powerful process. This involves identifying the boundaries we would like to either continue or modify with ourselves and others.

So how do we define a boundary? It is not a wall to isolate ourselves. Rather, a boundary is like a circle or fence that you get to draw around your life, allowing good in and keeping bad out. It can get bigger or smaller and can include gates or other openings depending on situations, but you get to choose who or what goes in or out. Boundaries can include people, situations, behaviors, thought processes—just about any component of life. When bad things happen beyond our control, we still get to choose a boundary that relates to how we will think, feel, and act. In other words, we cannot necessarily control what happens in our lives, but we can control our response or reaction to what happens in our lives.

On page 26 is a circle divided into the four categories of physical, social, emotional, and spiritual. Imagine that the circle is you and your life, and write your name in the middle.

Who and what do you want to be a part of your life in each of those four areas? Write a word or name to represent those things inside the circle.

Who and what do you want to limit or keep away from your life? Write a word or name to represent those things outside the circle. The farther from the circle you write represents the distance you would like them to be from you/your life.

For example, if you would like your friend, Ruth, to be part of your life, write her name inside the social part of the circle. If you have children, siblings, or others you would like to be part of your life, write their names or a general description inside your circle. If you would like to eat healthier or exercise more regularly, write those physical things inside the circle. If you would like values such as kindness, respect, self-care, and gratitude to be part of your life, write those things inside the emotional or spiritual part of the circle.

Likewise, if you have a friend or family member you would like to limit or distance yourself from, write their name outside your circle. If you have situations or circumstances you would like out of your circle (for example, unexpected visitors, chaotic relationships, excessive debt, disrespect), write those things in the white space outside the circle.

My Boundary Circle

Inside your boundary circle: Write who and what you would like to have *in* your life.

Outside your boundary circle: Write who and what you would like to limit or keep *out* of your life.

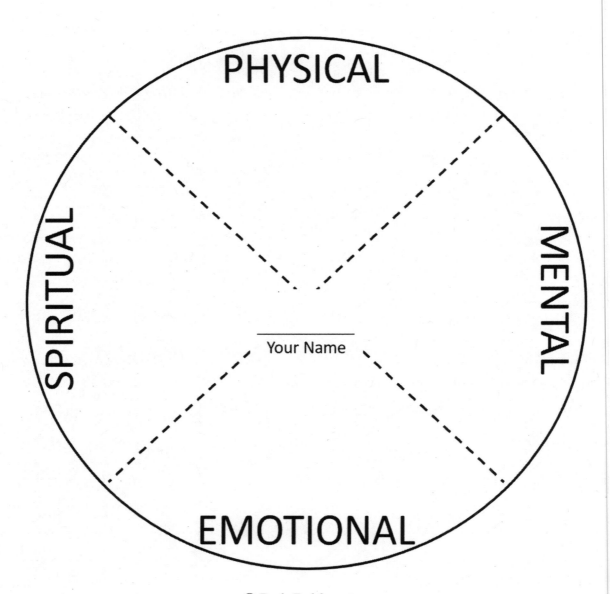

PHYSICAL

SPIRITUAL

MENTAL

_____
Your Name

EMOTIONAL

© Beth Bolthouse

3. **Embrace who you are now and who you will continue to become**

Life is not over for you, even though loss likes to lead you to think that way. You are growing and changing and becoming someone you are still getting to know. It is time to embrace the journey. Today you are learning more about yourself, and yet you still struggle at times. That is okay. Growth and healing are processes, so choosing to accept where you are and who you are *now* is good. Doing so will give you the ability to look forward to who you will choose to be tomorrow as the beliefs and boundaries you are working on continue to unfold and be reshaped.

Confidence

The third C is Confidence. Facing the future, learning more about ourselves, and naming how loss has changed us gives us the ability to increase our confidence. We can set small goals and feel successful; we can set big goals and adjust them as needed to avoid feeling we have failed. The goal you are working on in this workbook may become one you fulfill, or it may change and transform into something else altogether. Part of posttraumatic growth is choosing your thoughts and finding meaningful and positive ways to express those things to yourself and others. Embrace those attempts that don't work out as lessons and move forward. Don't stall or give up when a failure occurs—it is merely an opportunity to reflect and reconsider. Resilience is being built through developing greater confidence.

Identifying your needs and communicating them will also lead you into more confidence. Replacing "I should" with "I will" reduces shame and increases self-respect. Replacing "I have to" or "I can't" with "I choose to" or "I am not willing to" reminds us we have choices. Replacing "I should have" with "next time I can" reminds us of opportunities rather than obligations.

Making small choices in how we think and how we communicate with others gives us opportunities to grow in levels of confidence.

Take a few moments now to list out the people and situations (including debris) with whom and where you would like to have better boundaries, confidence, and courage.

_____   _____

_____   _____

_____   _____

_____   _____

_____   _____

REMEMBER: SMALL CHOICES EMPOWER BIGGER ONES!

Applying Life & Priorities

Here are opportunities that will help you sort through your beliefs, support your boundaries, and set goals for communicating and living your life:

Coping technique: Self-care

What would you like to do to take better care of you? Get more sleep? Take more walks? Cuddle with your cat? Watch a sunset? Read a good book? Exercise? Choose fruits and veggies over carbs and comfort food? Limit your exposure to some people, places, and things that are not beneficial to you. There are so many things we can choose that will nurture and value ourselves.

Make your own list of self-care choices:

♥ _____

♥ _____

♥ _____

♥ _____

♥ _____

♥ _____

♥ _____

♥ _____

Choose three practical ways from above in which you will practice self-care and keep track of how they affect your feelings and general outlook. Put a ☆ next to those three things.

Remind yourself of this important truth:

♥ I am worth loving and being cared for. ♥

Coping technique: Engaging gratitude

Gratitude helps us to find peace and joy in the midst of pain. Our circumstances may not have changed, but as the saying goes, gratitude changes our attitude—and perhaps the only thing we have control over *is* our attitude. Life happened, loss hurt us, grief took over our world, but we can still choose our focus. Gratitude empowers us in four areas of our life:

1. **Physical:** Increased relaxation, improved sleep, more energy, and less sickness

2. **Social:** New friendships, deeper relationships, increased confidence, and more positive connections

3. **Emotional:** Happier memories, increased resilience, increased sense of joy, an ability to maintain calm and peacefulness

4. **Spiritual:** Increased self-esteem, more aware of spiritual things, less materialistic, more optimistic, more other-centered

Writing your thoughts of gratitude helps to reinforce the reality of this focus and to encourage more resilience.

Using a journal, a calendar, or even sticky notes posted in a prominent spot, write one thought of gratitude each day for each of the four areas: physical, social, emotional, and spiritual.

SECTION 3: HEALTHIER RELATIONSHIPS WITH SELF AND OTHERS

How are you following through on your decision to practice self-care? Has it been difficult? Easy? Mixed? What feelings have you experienced after spending time nurturing yourself?

Many people express that self-care is foreign to them—they struggle to find something positive to do and often forget or procrastinate because they are unaccustomed to self-care. Self-care is not easy. Often, we have neglected to care for ourselves appropriately because we have been focused on managing grief. Yet self-care can be as simple as taking a few minutes to relax with a cup of tea or as complex as spending a day climbing a rock wall or anything in between. The great thing about self-care is you get to choose what is good for you and decide how and when you would like to engage in it.

We all have schedules and commitments, yet taking even a few meaningful moments each day for yourself can improve your health, give you a renewed sense of positivity, and provide a needed boost to your self-esteem. This is one of the most important ways to have a meaningful relationship with yourself. This is critical for your mental, emotional, spiritual, and physical health. You are worth it!

Writing messages of daily gratitude or affirmations of thankfulness can also be a positive self-care exercise. Although it was identified as a separate homework, it goes hand in hand with increasing the level of positive well-being that fosters peacefulness and counters the blues. As we discussed in Section 2, circumstances may stay the same, but choosing our attitude by engaging gratitude brings a sense of peace and joy so that we can face the hard things with increased confidence and strength.

Both of these activities (self-care and daily gratitude) are important to continue practicing so that they become an intricate part of the person you continue to become following the loss.

Lastly, are you becoming more aware of the debris or clutter that has been part of your life? Are you choosing positive responses, so the negative, unhealthy patterns become a thing of the past, and the true you continues to emerge?

Part of this process involves how we choose to behave toward people and situations. There are two factors involved: reacting vs. responding.

Reacting and Responding to Loss

It's easy to feel like things happen *to* us and to re-engage the clutter of victim thinking. When that occurs, emotions take over, and we react to people and situations. Our fight or flight kicks in, or we numb out, or some kind of impulsivity can take over—each leaving us feeling more helpless, afraid, anxious, and out of control.

Being intentional gives us the ability to have control within ourselves regardless of what is happening around us. It empowers us to respond from a place of thought and calmness, and the result is not allowing stress to take over. We may still feel stress, but being intentional in choosing our response helps us connect with inner strength and peacefulness. Instead of reacting out of fear or anxiety, we are able to respond from a place of truth and peace.

Career Coach Chrysta Bairre (2013) writes on her website that living with intention involves three components:

1. Being "purposeful in word and action," making "thoughtful choices," so your life has "meaning and is fulfilling."

2. Actively interacting and engaging with your life. She suggests that each morning when you wake up, ask yourself, "How am I going to make this day great?"

3. Responding instead of reacting; choosing "love instead of fear" (paras. 4-6).

Being intentional also allows us to stay in an adult mode. Transactional analysis, a theory developed by Dr. Eric Berne (1996), teaches that everyone operates from one of three aspects of our personality when engaging people or situations (Solomon, 2003, pp. 15-16):

1. As a critical or nurturing parent

2. As a free or rebellious child

3. As a rational adult

Being able to choose our responses in *positive* ways (as a nurturing parent, a free child, or as a rational adult) allows us to make decisions, be independent in our attitudes, and choose the direction we would like regardless of circumstances. What this means is that when someone hurts or offends me, I can choose to react (lash out, get even, hold a grudge, gossip) or respond (remain calm, not take things personally, let go of attachment to them, tell myself the truth about the situation, set a boundary). It takes practice to catch our reactions in time so that we can turn them into responses.

Using the chart on the next page, take a few moments to make notes about ways you can work on being more intentional in the physical, social, emotional, and spiritual areas of your life. Here are some examples:

1. **Physical:** Get extra sleep to reduce the tendency to be irritable.

2. **Social:** Listen to others more than talk about yourself.

3. **Emotional:** Pause and acknowledge your or others' feelings instead of impulsively reacting.

4. **Spiritual:** Choose to meditate or pray before making a decision.

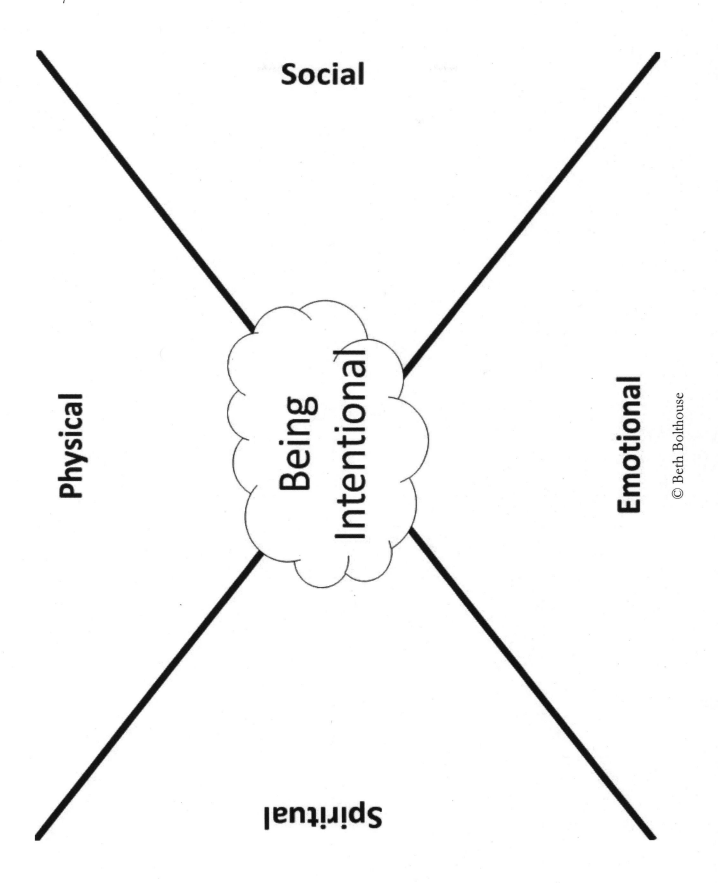

Mindfulness

Practicing mindfulness also helps us to be able to choose our responses and become more intentional in our relationships with ourselves and others.

Being mindful involves having an intentional focus on ourselves and how we view the world. When we experience a stressful, life-changing event or loss, it challenges our beliefs about the world, about ourselves, about others, and about our spirituality.

Mindfulness is much more than just positive thinking. It helps us to begin to choose what we will focus on and how we will implement the changes that have and continue to take place in our lives.

The Buddhist practice of mindfulness tells us to be aware of things happening in the present. Christianity teaches us that being mindful of "whatever is true, whatever is noble, whatever is right, whatever is pure, whatever is lovely, whatever is admirable—if anything is excellent or praiseworthy" will bring us peace (*NIV*, 1978/2011, Philippians 4:8-9). Many, if not all, the world's religions encourage some type of prayer or meditation, which is designed to increase peacefulness, leading to the conclusion that we inherently know to find peace through being mindful.

Yet stress and trauma disrupt that focus, and we find ourselves in the midst of emotional upheaval. Posttraumatic growth involves an awareness of ways we can choose to see our world differently and make new or different choices—in other words, being mindful.

Three factors can influence mindfulness:

1. **Self-talk**

Negative paths involve criticism, questioning myself, shame and blame, replaying events from a place of anxiety, taking things personally, wondering about things negatively, focusing on negatives, letting my feelings rule me, hopelessness, and depression.

Positive paths involve identifying truth, giving myself grace, recalling events when needed, taking things at face value, wondering about things positively, focusing on positives, having my feelings yet keeping them contained, increasing hopefulness, choosing joy in spite of circumstances.

When we become aware of negative self-talk, at any point, we can make an intentional choice to cross over to the positive path. It is often not easy—the "old tapes" from our hurts and our past may try to drown out the new truths we are implementing. Sometimes it helps to imagine putting up a STOP sign to interrupt the destructive thoughts so we can choose a healthy focus. It takes practice and perseverance over the course of our life, but the stronger our "new tapes" become, the less power and influence the old thinking patterns will have over us.

2. Memories and triggers

Many memories can cause us to ruminate on events and relationships in ways that increase fear and anxiety. We replay events over and over, increasing our stress level, and this takes us into reacting instead of mindfully responding. Triggers become part of the challenge as well. Things catch us off guard, and our sense of danger, insecurity, vulnerability, and fear is heightened. A trigger could be something simple, such as hearing part of a song on the radio, or as extreme as having a full-blown flashback that takes us right back into the past, as if it is happening in the present moment.

Rumination that is done *intentionally*, sometimes with the help of a close friend or a counselor, allows us to remember events within our level of control. Being mindful of memories and triggers involves controlling our breathing, staying focused or grounded in the present moment, keeping our perspective of the truth of the event, as well as the focus of the event in the past.

Journaling gives us an opportunity to release the memories and emotions that connect us to them so that they have a safe place to go. If you are unsure how to begin journaling, then start with making a list of feelings and memories. If memories we have written about return, we can remind ourselves we wrote about them and do not need to obsess about them. We can write additional thoughts as needed, further releasing the negative hold they have on us.

3. Practicing healthy boundaries

Being mindful also empowers us to choose to have healthy boundaries with ourselves and others. As discussed in Section 2, a boundary is like a circle or fence you get to put around your life, and you are in charge of it. It involves having integrity within yourself, being true to who you are, not changing yourself to please or "fix" others. These integrity choices ensure that you relate to yourself and others from a place of truth and honor. A boundary can protect you from people or situations that would sabotage your purpose. It can safeguard your heart as you continue to define your beliefs and yourself. It can help you say "No" without guilt and empower you to say "Yes" with joy.

Several years ago, I was part of a small group reading through Bruce Wilkinson's book, *Secrets of the Vine*. In it, he unpacks the analogy of John 14, where Jesus describes himself as the vine and his followers as branches. Our group decided it would be fun to drive up north and visit one of our Michigan vineyards to get a better understanding of this word picture. The man who oversees the vineyard took us around to each of the different grape varieties he was tending and growing and told us many details involved in working with the plants to produce the best wine possible.

Later that summer, while developing material for a boundaries group, I recalled the farmer's stories and the details he provided. It struck me that growing grapes, or grapevines, is a lot like cultivating healthy boundaries. Since that time, I've found it helpful to compare having boundaries with growing grapes.

Grapes can grow in any soil.	**Boundaries** exist in every situation.
Grapes take a few years to develop and grow into a healthy crop.	**Boundaries** take years to develop into consistent healthy patterns.
Grapes have to be maintained by regular pruning. This involves getting rid of the "dead wood" that looks like the grapevine yet will take over the plant and stunt new growth and sabotage the vine.	**Boundaries** have to be maintained by accountability and changing habit patterns to prune the toxicity out of our lives. If we don't prune, old habits emerge and stunt us, and we end up going back to old unhealthy ways of living. We become sour grapes!
Grapes are trained by the gardener to grow in the best direction regardless of weather conditions.	We have to be trained to learn healthy **boundaries**, to look to God or our higher power for direction, and ensure our true self continues to take shape regardless of circumstances.
Grapes' roots will search for water and go as deep and far as they need to find it.	A person with healthy **boundaries** will search for wisdom and go as deep and far as they need to find it. It is a process worth searching for.

In their book *Boundaries: When to Say Yes, How to Say No to Take Control of Your Life*, Henry Cloud and John Townsend (1992, pp. 144-150) identify four types of people we encounter who will challenge our boundaries:

1. **Compliant people** have "fuzzy" boundaries. They don't like to rock the boat and will do whatever they can to get along; they change themselves to fit into their environment. They don't like to hurt someone else's feelings, fear being abandoned, being seen as bad or selfish, and like to be taken care of.

2. **Avoidant people** don't like to ask for help, have difficulty identifying their own needs, keep others at a distance, and think of boundaries as walls that tend to be rigid.

3. **Controllers** don't respect the limits of others. They resist taking responsibility for their own lives and then feel the need to control others. They can't hear "no" (which is different than being able to say "no"). They can be manipulative or aggressive, tend to be self-focused, and use guilt messages to get what they want.

4. **Nonresponsive people** tend to be critical toward others and self-absorbed. They don't care about the needs of others, which is why many will withhold in relationships.

You may ask, what does all this have to do with posttraumatic growth? The reason this information is included in this workbook is that, after a life-changing stressor or trauma, we struggle with knowing what is truthful and/or who to trust; our security has been disrupted; life, as we knew it and believed it to be, has been shattered. Identifying who we encounter and recognizing healthy boundary options is important as we continue to grow in relationship with ourselves and others. It empowers us to be intentional, to choose who and what we want in our lives, and it reinforces the importance of living intentionally.

Take a look at the boundary circle you made notes on in Section 2 and use the next page to identify specific boundaries you would like to implement.

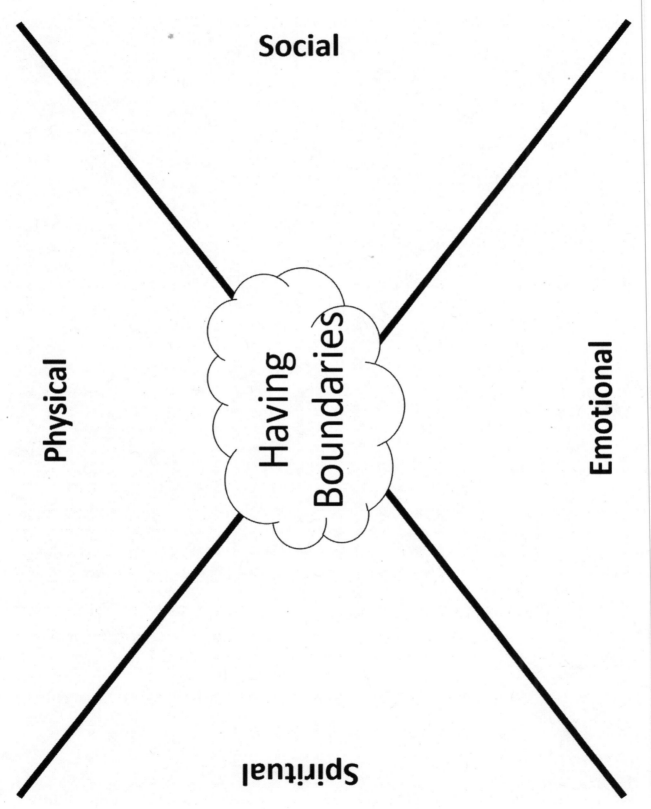

Social

Physical

Having Boundaries

Emotional

Spiritual

Five things that can disrupt the growth and transformation that is taking place after our loss(es) as well as interfere with developing healthier relationship patterns are:

1. **Fear:** It is difficult to know the truth and identify healthy choices when fear is in control. It reinforces anxiety and prevents us from focusing on who we are now.

2. **Shame:** Shame disrupts the empowering language we have been learning and takes us back into the next disruption, blame.

3. **Blame:** When we experience a stressful, traumatic loss, we look for someone or something to blame. This focus can become a spiral into bitterness and resentment, and it distracts us from our own healing.

4. **Entitlement:** Where we think the world owes us and we deserve only good experiences, we are in our own reality.

5. **False Guilt:** False guilt happens when we are looking for someone or something to blame, and we decide it needs to be us. Most of the guilt we have when we grieve is regret, not guilt. We regret that this happened, or that we did not make a different choice, or were not there to help our loved one in the way we would have liked to. There are so many things we regret. Yet, we cannot go back and change things, either. Taking on guilt is a hopeless and helpless miry pit that keeps us from growing and healing. It is futile and benefits no one.

How do these five areas play out in your own life? And are you ready to take yourself out of these zones so you can engage truth in relationship with yourself?

What boundaries are you going to begin using within your thinking patterns to keep you from falling into each of these self-destructive pits?

Write out one positive boundary you would like to have with yourself in each of these areas. Perhaps it will be a truth statement, self-talk, an action item, or any boundary you would like to have to keep these five disruptions from being part of your life.

1. Fear _____

2. Shame _____

3. Blame _____

4. Entitlement _____

5. False Guilt _____

Applying Healthier Relationships with Self and Others

Coping technique: Saying "no"

Take time to practice saying "No" aloud and then use it when appropriate. Here are a few examples:

- No thank you.
- Not now.
- I will no longer ...
- I am not able to ...
- That is not something I am interested in.
- I will not ...
- No.

Coping technique: Daily affirmations

Telling ourselves the truth each day does three things as we grow in having healthy relationships with ourselves and others:

1. It encourages mindfulness.
2. It keeps us focused on positive self-talk.
3. It reinforces boundary setting and maintaining.

On the next two pages is a list of daily affirmations—one for every day of the month. Take each one, look at yourself in a mirror, and say it out loud, determined, and with a smile. Practice being powerful. Claim these statements as truth for your life.

DAILY AFFIRMATIONS

1. I will remember that I am doing the best I can and do not need to be "perfect."

2. I am a caring, compassionate person and am able to be loving toward myself as well as others.

3. My feelings matter; therefore, I will be sure to acknowledge them in safe ways so they do not overwhelm me.

4. I have a compassionate heart; this includes compassion for myself.

5. I will remember that God loves me and does not expect me to be perfect.

6. I am lovingly tolerant of myself and my needs.

7. My needs for self-care are important; therefore, I will do something kind for myself at least once a day.

8. I will remember that everyone is going through a challenge, including me, and I will be patient with myself and others.

9. I will remember that giving tender loving care to myself helps me have hope.

10. I will let go of guilt and choose to forgive myself and be kind and respectful to me.

11. I will treasure my own heart and be gentle with myself.

12. I will do at least one thing each day that brings me joy to ensure I am loving myself well.

13. At the end of each day, I will remember that I am worth loving and not give in to guilt or regret.

14. I will treat myself with kindness and gentleness, remembering I am human and do not need to be perfect.

15. Each morning I will appreciate being alive and giving love to myself and others.

16. My life is no one else's; I get to choose how I want to live and what is meaningful to me.

17. My spirituality brings me deep peace and reassures me that I am loved and loveable.

18. I will honor the many gifts which I've been given and be good to myself and others.

19. I can choose to cherish and nurture myself. This helps me feel loved and love others.

20. I will let go of shaming thoughts and choose to be kind to myself and others.

21. I am a unique and valuable person—that is the truth I wake up to each day.

22. My life will have challenges, but these challenges do not define me.

23. I will let go of judging and criticizing myself so that I can be free to enjoy who I am and give others opportunities to be who they are.

24. Joy increases as I tell myself the truth—that I am a person who brings value, significance, and meaning to others.

25. I am a difference maker—my presence in the lives of others helps them feel worthwhile and gives them hope.

26. My life matters; therefore, I will choose things that are loving and caring for myself.

27. Today is the only day I need to focus on; I will let go of worrying about tomorrow.

28. Today I will take time to smile in the mirror and tell myself that I am loved.

29. My feelings matter; I will be gentle and kind to myself and honor my emotional life.

30. I am willing to reach out for support, even if it means reaching out to more than one person until I find a safe person to connect with.

31. I will choose gratitude each day to remind myself that life is worth living, and I can find meaning and purpose, even when my feelings try to take me into a negative place.

SECTION 4: PERSONAL STRENGTH

Reviewing

As we begin Section 4, let's revisit two quotes that relate to our work. The first is related to posttraumatic growth. Tedeschi & Calhoun (2004), the pioneers of posttraumatic growth, define it as the phenomenon of positive change that can result from a struggle with highly challenging life circumstances.

When we look back at our loss and the intense and negative effects it had on our lives and on us personally, it is important to see there are also positive changes taking place as a result. Many of these changes unfold slowly and cautiously over time. We have had to make so many adjustments, and if we are honest, we will admit we tend to resist those even though we know they are important and necessary. Life as we used to know it does not exist in the same way as it did before the loss. Adapting to these changes is a process, a transition, and we are so much more aware now of the ways traumatic loss impacts our lives.

To think that positive change takes place after trauma is a truly surprising phenomenon, as Tedeschi & Calhoun describe—one which we may marvel at as we review the months and years since our loss and one in which perhaps we continue to feel little and big twinges of grief.

Leo Buscaglia (1994) said, "The only lasting trauma is the one we suffer without positive change" (p. 63). Imagine if we had been unwilling to adapt or adjust and had refused to allow our loss to bring positive change and growth into our lives. We would be stuck, paralyzed by the trauma, and our lives would have come to some type of standstill, with no hope or joy or thought of a future. That is what trauma strives to do—ruin us and the life we had *hoped* for. Yet, being intentional about embracing the positive changes that are possible allows us to connect with new amazing possibilities that lie ahead.

Up to this point, we have:

- Identified how our families of origin handled loss and grief

- Uncovered the physical, social, emotional, and spiritual changes and growth opportunities which resulted from our loss(es)

- Learned about traumatic grief and ways to begin managing it

- Discussed "secondary losses"

- Identified a 6-month goal and started working toward achieving it

- Identified the strengths of our individual personality type

- Discussed both negative and positive ways we have adapted to our loss(es)

- We have also learned about the significance of empowering language:

  o **Challenge** our beliefs about ourselves, others, the world, spirituality, and even the loss itself

  o **Courage** to accept the consequences of the loss, make changes with ourselves and others, and begin embracing who we are now as well as who we are continuing to become

  o **Confidence** to set a short-term goal, communicate our needs, and look forward to a future

- Invited more self-care and gratitude into our lives

- Discussed the benefits of being intentional and mindful

- Learned about relational styles and boundary setting

- Discussed what can keep us from healthy living (fear, shame, blame, entitlement, and false guilt)

- Realized the significance of daily affirmations

Changes You Are Noticing

As we begin Section 4, let's also take a few moments to identify changes you are noticing in your life in the four areas of physical, social, emotional, and spiritual. On the following page, note in each of the four areas ways you are starting to change.

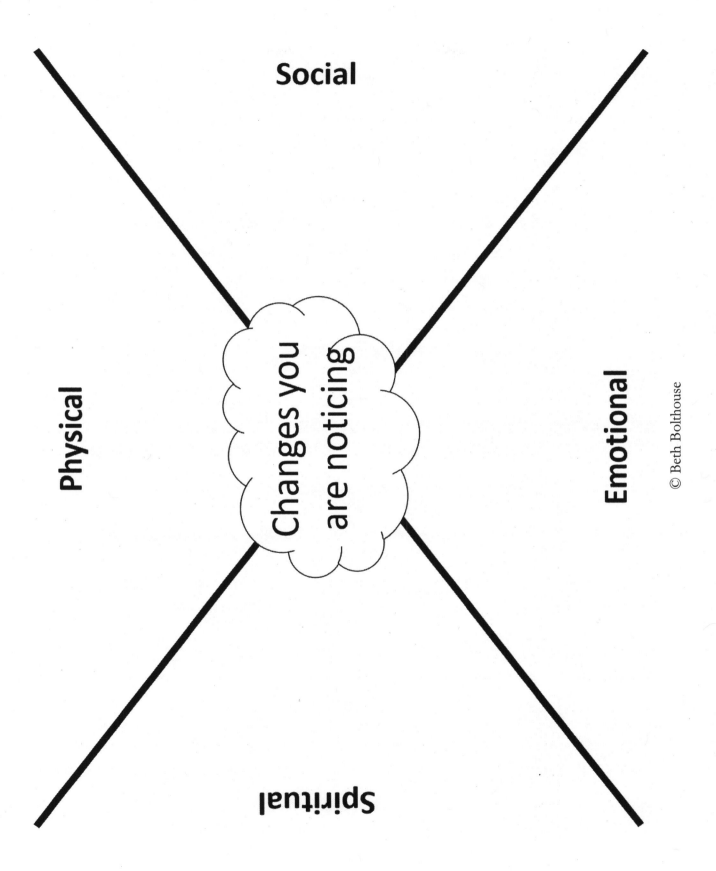

Finding Meaning and Purpose in the Loss

The ways we have changed as a result of grief can be one of the more difficult things to wrap our minds around. The loss is not something we chose; it has been difficult, painful, hurtful, and wreaked havoc in our lives in various ways. Our lives have been turned upside down—the proverbial rug has been ripped from beneath our feet. As a result, it can feel as though we are lost without the safety and security we knew before the loss. Finding purpose and meaning can be a challenge. We may not want to imagine that the loss could ever make sense; it may be we search for answers to the "why" question, yet there are none.

When you consider finding purpose in the loss, what type of reactions do you have? _____

_____

_____

_____

What types of "why" questions have you asked?_____

_____

_____

_____

_____

_____

The truth is that "why" may never be answered. But if we ask "how," we can begin to expand our views of the loss and bring meaning into something that otherwise has none.

Here are some "how" questions to consider and respond to:

How has this loss impacted my life? _____

_____

_____

_____

_____

How do I respond to others who are experiencing loss now that I have experienced this loss?_____

_____

_____

_____

_____

How has this loss changed me?_____

_____

_____

_____

_____

How can I make a difference in the world because of my loss?_____

_____

_____

_____

_____

How can I change my future based on this loss?_____

_____

_____

_____

_____

How do I choose to think about my loss?_____

_____

_____

_____

_____

Continuing Bonds

Continuing bonds are ways we continue to stay connected to our loved ones after they have died. They are not here physically, yet our relationship with them continues in different ways than when they were alive.

Continuing bonds may include completing unfinished tasks that were planned prior to his/her death or the traumatic event, talking or writing to the deceased, engaging in rituals where the deceased is remembered or recalled, reflecting on relationship history, or moving away from what the deceased would have done or chosen.

In addition to finding continuing bonds with the person who has died, another person you may need to establish continuing bonds with is—yourself! When we experience a traumatic loss, we lose who we were before the loss. It is important to think about who that person was, use journaling to reflect on our history and on unfinished tasks that we would either say goodbye to or bring into our present lives in some way. Rituals such as speaking daily affirmations or engaging in self-care are ways we bring our wounded self into the present and integrate healing into the pain we have experienced. Writing a letter to your loved one, yourself (or both), or another person involved in the loss can be a meaningful way to express things you would like to say.

In the space provided below, write a letter expressing the things you would like to say to your loved one, or yourself, or another person involved in the loss. Share how you are healing from what happened and anything else you would like to convey: _____

_____

_____

_____

_____

_____

_____

_____

_____

_____

_____

_____

_____

_____

Meaning-Making

Meaning-making is similar to finding purpose, yet it challenges us to identify our belief system before the loss and look for ways it has evolved or stayed the same after our loss. Each of the four areas we have been focusing on in this group—emotional, spiritual, social, physical—could be broken down into lists of values or beliefs.

- **Physical:** What do I believe about my environment? How secure do I feel now?

- **Social:** What do I believe about others? How trusting am I of others?

- **Emotional:** What do I believe about my feelings? How would I like to express them?

- **Spiritual:** What do I believe about God or spirituality? How does this belief integrate with my life?

On the following page, use three different colors of markers or pencils to identify:

1. How I experienced my loss in the first year (in relation to each area)
2. How my grief experience has changed to this point
3. What I hope my loss will mean to me a year from now

Social

What do I believe or value about others?

Physical

What do I believe or value about my environment?

Meaning-Making

Ways my beliefs and values have evolved since the loss

Emotional

What do I believe or value about emotion?

© Beth Bolthouse

Spiritual

What do I believe or value about God/spirituality?

OPTIONS FOR SMALL GROUPS

1. **Pipe Cleaners**

   Group participants select four different color pipe cleaners for themselves. Ask them to form them into a shape or connect them in some way that represents how they experienced their loss in the first year. Next, ask them to modify their concept to reflect how their grief experience has changed to this present time and talk about the changes they made. Finally, ask them to modify or reshape the design once more to identify what they would like their loss will mean to them in a year.

2. **Soft Clay**

   Have group participants use multiple colors of clay (their choice) to make a representation of how they experienced their loss in the first year; then modify the design to reflect how their grief has changed to the present time. Then ask them to reshape or modify it to reflect what they would like their loss to mean in a year.

3. **Paper and Colored Writing Utensils**

   During this exercise, distribute paper and colored markers or crayons to each participant. Ask them to draw a depiction of how they experienced their loss in the first year. Their drawing may be an abstract or stick figures or various objects and words, using a variety of colors that identify their loss experience. After completing this, ask them to share with the group. Then ask them to take some time to modify their depiction to reflect how their grief has changed to the present time and share with the group. Finally, ask them to modify it again in some way to reflect what they would like their loss to look like in a year.

   (This can also be meaningful when the group is meeting virtually. Ask group participants to bring paper and colored markers or crayons with them in preparation for this session. Participants can share with others by holding their drawings up to the camera.)

Developing an Identity/Purpose Statement

We have discussed many ways we have changed as a result of our loss and identified the significance of how trauma is facilitating positive growth.

Now we will put together an Identity or Purpose Statement—one that will affirm who you are, how you relate to others, and the ways you are motivated and energized for the future.

Author Dan Miller, in his book *48 Days to the Work You Love*, writes: "Before I can tell my life what I want to do with it, I must listen for that voice telling me who I am" (2010, p. 40).

Who is the voice in your head telling you who you are? Is it the loss reminding you of the negative, hurtful, depressing things that happened as a result of your loss? Or are you becoming your own voice, telling the loss that although you have been wounded and your life has been forever changed, you have positive choices for now and the future? That you are choosing growth and opportunities and healthy relationships?

Miller identifies three things we need to determine as we develop our purpose and identity (p. 58). Write in each area below what is true about you:

1. My skills and abilities are (what I like to do) _____

   _____

   _____

   _____

2. My personality traits are (how I relate to people and situations) _____

   _____

   _____

   _____

3. My values, dreams, and passions are (what motivates me and energizes me) _____

   _____

   _____

   _____

Now, combine these three lists into one or two sentences:

I am a person who _____

_____

_____

_____

_____

_____

_____

_____

_____

_____

_____

_____

_____

Applying Personal Strength

Coping techniques

Coping technique: Look in the mirror every morning and say your personal identity statement aloud. You may also wish to tape it to your mirror or in a location you will see each day.

Coping technique: Continue to make your gratitude list each day.

Coping technique: Continue to work on or revise your 6-month goal.

SECTION 5: NEW POSSIBILITIES

I n the previous section, we explored the ways we have changed since our loss. We wrote a personal identity statement that reflects who we are now and who we continue to become.

In this section, we will look at the process of posttraumatic growth and integrate what we have worked on thus far to identify the new possibilities ahead.

Posttraumatic growth, as we have discussed, is the process of transformative change that takes place after a devastating life event or loss. It takes time to work through and, in many ways, is a life-long process rather than a result to be achieved.

Two previously mentioned researchers who first developed the theory of posttraumatic growth, Richard Tedeschi and Lawrence Calhoun (1996), put together the Post Traumatic Growth Inventory that measures the positive changes, which a person experiences after a life-altering loss or trauma, in the following five areas: appreciation for life, relationship with self and others, personal strength, new possibilities, and spiritual development.

This workbook has taken those five areas and explored various aspects of loss using counseling techniques to help you recognize, identify, and continue to move forward in posttraumatic growth.

Two key components which we are going to discuss in this section are:

- Changed perception of self
- Changed philosophy of life

As you read below and respond to questions, use this time to reflect not only on the past and present changes but also on how you would like your future to be as your life unfolds.

Changed Perception of Self

Personal strength

In the initial weeks and months following a traumatic loss, we begin to realize we are not who we once were. We may feel lost, alone, and more helpless than we ever thought we could feel. Today as you engage with posttraumatic growth, it is important to realize that the vulnerabilities that dominated your life are becoming a sense of personal strength.

As Tedeschi & Moore write in their *Handbook of Posttraumatic Growth* (2006), the growth you are experiencing is "vulnerable yet stronger." It is as if to say, "I am more vulnerable than I thought, but much stronger than I ever imagined" (p. 5). You have gone through a horrific experience, one in which perhaps others may struggle to continue living. Yet you have survived, you are overcoming, and you are realizing there is a strength you never knew you had, even in the midst of great vulnerability.

New possibilities

Things have changed; life is not what it used to be; and along with that, there are opportunities to discover hobbies, interests, and activities you perhaps never or rarely participated in. These are important days, ones that open up new doors and new pathways in your life. Perhaps it is time to explore going back to school, attending an art class, taking dance lessons, or getting involved in a gym. Maybe there are volunteer opportunities that will give you a deeper awareness of who you are now and ways you can give back. However you choose to be open to new options, you can find meaning and significance through these opportunities that give you a deeper sense of purpose.

Relating to others

For most people who have experienced significant loss, relationships are different now, even as you are different. You see others through a different lens, and you feel compassion for others in ways or degrees that are new; perhaps you feel closer to some folks and not as connected to others. There may be a sense of freedom to be yourself more now than you have ever been able to be. Many grievers express their filters are different now—they say what they think, don't put up with trivial concerns, focus on what matters, and choose to be around people who are authentic because they feel more authentic themselves.

Changed Philosophy of Life

Sense of priorities

You love what matters now. You focus on things that make a difference. Authenticity becomes the norm because you've been through something that shattered your world. People and things take on different order in your life than they used to. You invest your energy and your focus on things that matter.

Greater appreciation

Along with changing priorities, you have a deeper level of appreciation for what matters. The things that you used to take for granted have more meaning. You choose gratitude and thankfulness for others, including strangers. You are more aware of how, suddenly and without warning, life can change. The little things bring you joy, and the big things perhaps have a different place than they used to.

Changing or deepening spirituality

Your soul has been affected by this loss; therefore, your spiritual self is more alert and aware than before. You may search for meaning or realize that what used to feed your soul has left you hungry for something different. Sometimes a person's belief in God is intensified, and other times there is an ongoing struggle. Challenging our beliefs can lead us into a type of spiritual renewal, which increases hope and peace.

Preparedness

We realize we have survived the worst, and we have a heightened sense of needing to be prepared for whatever may happen in the future. We are no longer naïve; the world is not what we used to imagine; we are realistic now and are making changes in order to survive whatever the future may bring.

What we are left with is the realization that we are resilient. We have adapted in the face of adversity; we have chosen each day to live that day; we have set goals for the future and modified them as needed; we have taken our life and relationships by the reins and made decisions that make a difference.

"Recovery" is a term used by people who want to get back to how life was before a loss. We recognize that it will never happen. We are forever different, yet that is not a bad thing. We are growing; we are becoming; we are changing; we are reconfiguring our thoughts, beliefs, and behaviors so that we can handle whatever the future brings.

Reflecting

Take a few moments to respond to the following questions.

Imagine what your life would be like or what you would have become if this had not happened? _____

_____

_____

_____

_____

Are there any benefits to the grief experience? _____

_____

_____

_____

What has this loss opened your eyes to see differently?_____

_____

_____

_____

_____

What are you experiencing differently in your life now? _____

_____

_____

_____

_____

How do you continue to change or evolve since the loss?_____

_____

_____

_____

_____

Letter to Myself

Using the template below, write a letter to yourself expressing how things *were*, how things *have changed*, and *everything in between.*

Dear _____,

I suffered an unimaginable loss _____ months/years ago. It left me feeling _____
_____

It has changed _____
_____

It was hard to believe life would ever be good again. But today, I can affirm that the following positives have taken place in my life:

      Physical: _____

      Emotional: _____

      Social: _____

      Spiritual: _____

In addition, I am evolving into a person who (incorporate from purpose statement in Section 4 along with any other positive affirmations) _____
_____
_____
_____

Although life has changed, and I continue to have times when I miss _____, my eyes have been opened to see the following changes:

      Physical: _____

      Emotional: _____

      Social: _____

      Spiritual: _____

If I had not gone through this loss, I would still be _____
_____

I can see now that grieving _____ has had some benefits for me, including the following:

Physical: _____

Emotional: _____

Social: _____

Spiritual: _____

I will continue to love myself and look to the future with hope, even as I continue to miss

_____,

knowing that I am a better person because of what I have gone through.

With Love,

Me

Applying New Possibilities

Coping technique: Continuing positive growth

Accountability—I will utilize the following person(s) and activities to ensure I continue to grow in positive ways: _____

_____

_____

_____

_____

Mindfulness—I will continue using the following mindfulness techniques: _____

_____

_____

_____

Outreach—I will give back or volunteer in the following way(s): _____

_____

_____

_____

Legacy—I will continue to develop my legacy in the following way(s): _____

_____

_____

_____

SECTION 6: SPIRITUAL GROWTH

Attachments

Grief is defined as "a wound to our attachment system, and the responses to separation and a broken attachment are often emotional ones" (Winokuer & Harris, 2012, p. 119).

When we consider that loss breaks an attachment to a person or situation that mattered to us in some way, it helps us put losses into perspective. William Worden (2009), a renowned grief expert, has identified the following five important factors related to attachment that directly or indirectly influence how we move through grief (p. 58-59):

1. **The strength of the attachment:** Grief is a reflection of the love relationship; therefore, it is important to note that the more deeply we have loved, the greater the intensity of our grief.

2. **The security of the attachment:** The loss of a person relates directly to a sense of positive or negative well-being. If we relied on the person who died for self-esteem or depended on a circumstance or situation for security, then in loss, we find we have lost our resource for feeling okay about ourselves and our world.

3. **The ambivalence of the attachment:** When the relationship has many positive and negative aspects, false guilt can become prominent after a loss. We will question ourselves, wondering if we did enough or were enough, yet simultaneously feeling anger at the person who died or the situation that caused us pain.

4. **The conflicts with the person or situation:** Both past and present conflicts can result in a wide range of unfinished business. If the loss was sudden and unexpected, this could lead a person to struggle with intense guilt and regret.

5. **The dependency on the person or situation:** It is difficult to adapt to the loss when we have been dependent on the person or situation to meet our daily needs or function on a day-to-day basis.

As Winokuer & Harris write, "attachment relationships are linked to our primary, instinctual need to be close to significant others in order to feel safe and to feel a sense of 'anchoring' in our world" (2016, pp. 26-27).

What brings you security? _____

What anchors you to your world? _____

The level of safety and security those above-mentioned people or situations bring are important and matter. They encourage us to grow closer, to attach stronger, to take risks of intimacy and trust. And when a loss occurs within those connections, the safety and very foundation on which we lived is shattered.

Our spirituality is challenged. If we have faith in God, we may find ourselves questioning more, doubting more, being angry, disengaging from prayer, not interested in connecting with others of the same faith base. The church or synagogue may lose its appeal or become a trigger rather than a place of worship and connection.

If we were atheists or uncertain of whether God exists or is involved in the world before our loss, we may find ourselves either more certain than ever there is no God, or we may begin searching, looking for some kind of meaning to the tragedy in our lives.

The attachment styles we grew up with and grew into over the course of our life are factors in the ways we respond to grief. Below are descriptions of attachment styles and how they typically influence grieving. Which one(s) do you connect with?

Secure attachment

If we grew up in a secure or healthy home environment where we learned to trust and know our caregivers would come through for us, we are not afraid to ask for what we need and expect those needs to be met. In grief, we reach out for help when we need it and do not waste time with people who are not supportive. Even in the midst of deep pain, we can have a sense of resilience, knowing that we can find the help we need to get through this stress and trauma. We may seek God more than ever or long to spend time with others who believe as we do and therefore derive comfort and encouragement that is more meaningful than it ever was. We may reach out for prayer or assistance or other types of support and find others coming through in amazing and powerful ways.

Ambivalent attachment

If we grew up with caregivers who were inconsistent in meeting our needs, we might have developed ambivalent attachment. This attachment style inhibits our ability to believe we can get our needs met, and often we struggle with feeling lovable and worthy of being cared for. In grief, we tend to struggle to reach out or may feel we deserve the pain and should not reach out. We do not trust others will come through for us. We doubt whether our prayers would make any difference. In fact, we don't really trust that God is with us or would ever come through for us.

Fearful avoidant attachment

If we find it difficult to trust others, even putting up walls to guard against being rejected, we may have had insensitive caregivers, even rejecting our needs. He or she may have been unavailable or withdrawn from us during times of stress or difficulties. These experiences may have resulted in our having more of a fearful avoidant type of attachment with others. When we grieve, we are not sure who to trust. Perhaps those we hoped would be of support have gone on with their lives, and that has led us to feel more alone and even less trusting of others to be there. We see God through the lens of rejection, too. We feel God is not interested in what we are going through or doesn't care. (If God cared, such a devastating thing would not have happened, would it?)

Dismissive avoidant attachment

If we grew up with caregivers who mistreated or frightened us, this experience taught us that nothing and no one is safe. We grew up feeling vulnerable and, therefore, may struggle with what is termed dismissive avoidant. We fear being too vulnerable, so we do not get close to others. In grief, the very thing we need is the very thing we are afraid of, so we tend to go through the pain alone, afraid of more pain from others, and often situations occur while we are hurting that can reinforce the danger of being vulnerable. Religion is nothing more than fearing God who punishes. We may feel what happened is our fault or some kind of condemnation. We may do our best to keep a distance from anything having to do with religious people or situations.

As you read through the above descriptions of attachment styles and grief, which one(s) do you connect with and why? _____

_____

_____

_____

_____

_____

The good news is we are growing, changing, engaging in positive growth. A new self is emerging through the process of posttraumatic growth. We can explore new ways of seeing ourselves and others, even while going through the negative effects of our loss. We can explore spirituality in ways that are meaningful to us. We can look for authentic caring and genuine love from people and likewise express those traits to others who are hurting.

There are opportunities for positive growth that we did not realize before, and these give us opportunities to honor our grief in ways that value us and our world.

We also find that *resilience* increases as we focus on going on with life after the stress and trauma we have experienced. We do not move on, away from grief; instead, we prioritize what matters, focus on our strengths, and continue to redefine ourselves and our world.

Just like the person who said, "I am not what happened to me. I am what I choose to become," we have opportunities, and we have choices—opportunities to be intentional and live life in positive ways. We realize that loss will happen in the future, and perhaps wonder, what will I do with future grief?.

"What Will I Do With Future Grief?"

This question cannot be answered until we respond to the following:

- What needs do we have now that we can expect to be met?

- What new way do we choose to see ourselves today?

- What is a sign of positive growth that I recognize right now?

- What are my strengths? What matters to me now?

Take a few moments to respond to each of these questions on the following pages as they relate to the four areas of your life: physical, social, spiritual, emotional.

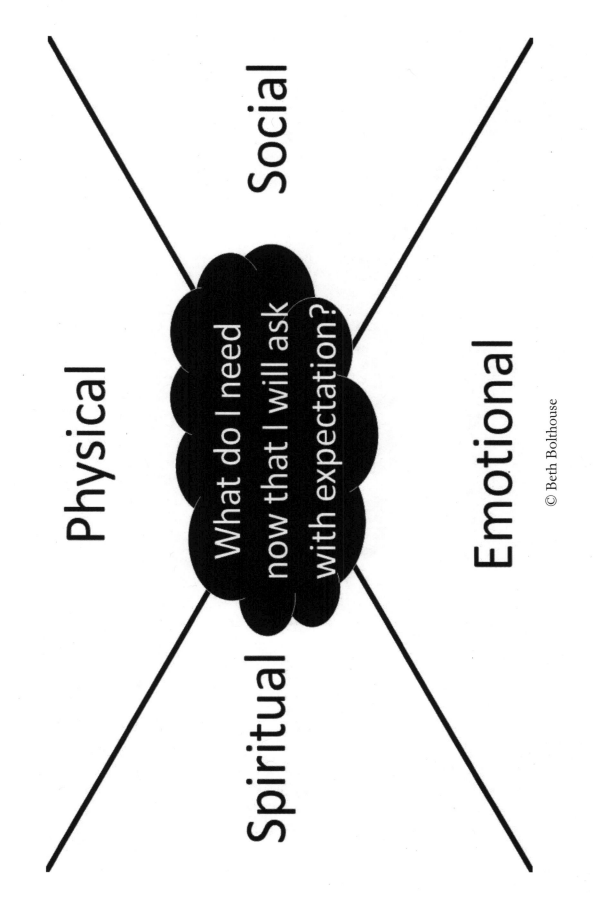

Physical

Social

Spiritual

Emotional

What do I need now that I will ask with expectation?

© Beth Bolthouse

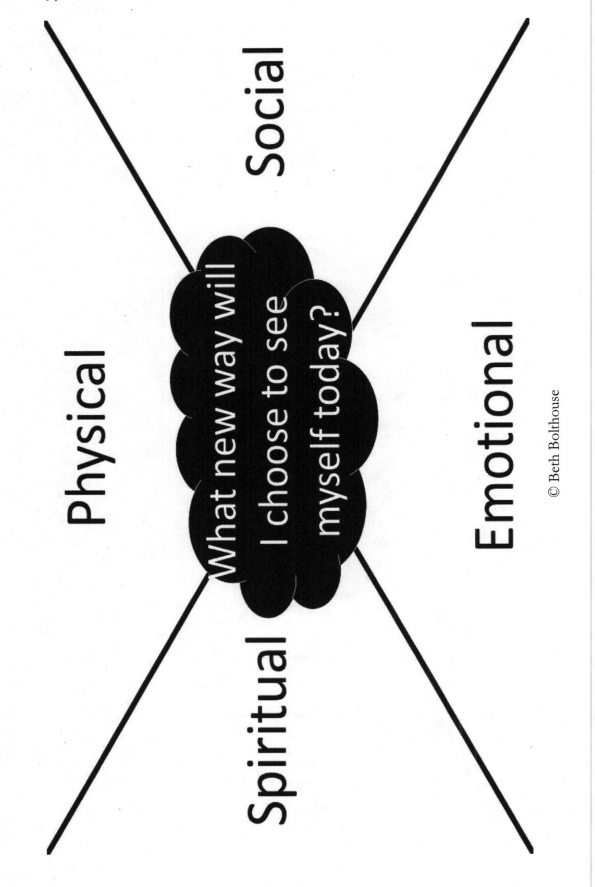

Social

Physical

Spiritual

Emotional

What new way will I choose to see myself today?

© Beth Bolthouse

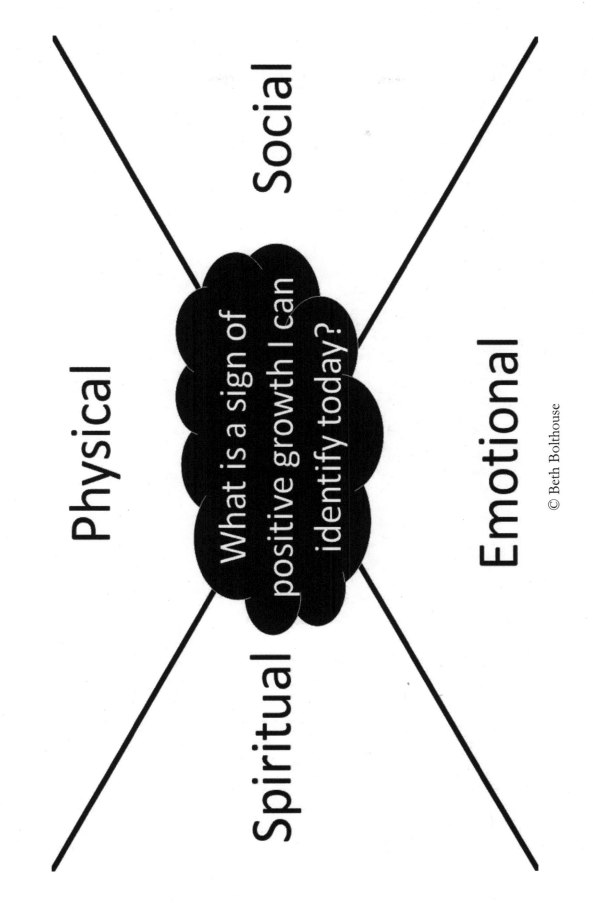

Social

Physical

Spiritual

Emotional

What is a sign of positive growth I can identify today?

© Beth Bolthouse

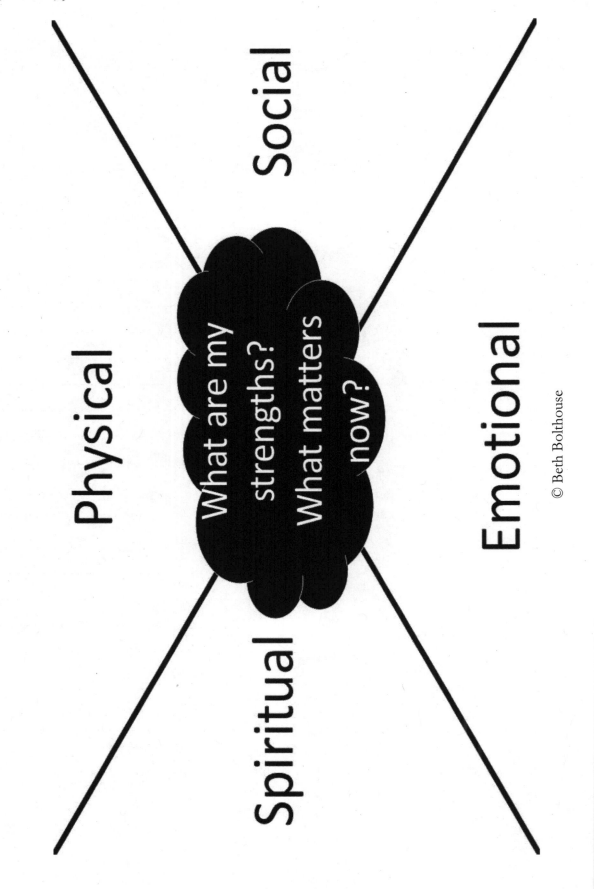

Physical

Social

Spiritual

Emotional

What are my strengths? What matters now?

© Beth Bolthouse

Continuing On

We have come to the place in this workbook where you find a fork in the road. One path is not better or worse than the other. Each path is simply a new direction, and choosing one will lead you forward. Turning away from this choice and going back into the past ways of relating and living will sabotage the life you are allowing to continue to emerge and the new self you are becoming.

As you reflect on this journey, what have you learned most about yourself? _____

_____

_____

_____

_____

_____

_____

_____

_____

_____

_____

How did your 6-month goal unfold? Did you make changes and adjust things as needed based on how you have been growing? Did you give yourself permission to let go and choose something different? Did you decide it was worth completing and continue working toward it? Write a few thoughts about this part of the journey: _____

_____

_____

_____

_____

_____

_____

_____

_____

How will you continue the process of posttraumatic growth? What will help you stay focused on making healthy choices, staying true to yourself, living life in meaningful ways while still allowing grief its place when necessary? _____

_____

_____

_____

_____

_____

_____

_____

_____

_____

_____

_____

_____

The future makes no guarantees. We know there are difficult times ahead, just as there will be joyful experiences. We get to choose how we adapt, relate, think, explore, and develop—just as we have been doing throughout this workbook.

Applying Spiritual Growth

Coping technique: The 4 Rs

1. **Revive** yourself daily with gratitude.

2. **Regenerate** relationships through healthy boundaries with yourself and others.

3. **Renew** yourself regularly through meaningful self-care; engage your spirituality, and allow positive relationships to flourish.

4. **Remember** resilience is what develops and increases as we continue to choose posttraumatic growth.

Appendix: Feeling Words List

abandoned	distraught	ignored	pleasant	tenacious
adequate	disturbed	immortal	pleased	tenuous
adamant	dominated	impressed	precarious	tense
affectionate	divided	infatuated	pressured	tentative
agonized	dubious	infuriated	pretty	terrible
ambivalent		inspired	prim	terrified
annoyed	eager	intimidated	prissy	threatened
anxious	ecstatic	isolated	proud	tired
apathetic	electrified			thwarted
astounded	empty	jealous	quarrelsome	troubled
awed	enchanted	joyous	queer	
	energetic	jumpy		ugly
bad	envious		rage	uneasy
beautiful	excited	kind	rapture	unsettled
betrayed	evil	keen	refreshed	
bitter	exasperated		rejected	violent
bold	exhausted	laconic	relieved	vehement
bored		lazy	relaxed	vital
brave	fascinated	lecherous	remorse	vulnerable
burdened	fawning	left out	restless	vivacious
	fearful	licentious	reverent	
calm	flustered	lonely	rewarded	wicked
capable	foolish	longing	righteous	wonderful
captivated	fragmented	love		weepy
challenged	frazzled	low	sad	worried
charmed	frustrated		sated	
cheated	frightened	mad	satisfied	zany
cheerful	full	maudlin	scared	zapped
childish	furious	mean	screwed up	
clever		melancholy	servile	
combative	glad	miserable	settled	
competitive	good	mystical	sexy	
condemned	gratified		shocked	
confused	greedy	naughty	silly	
conspicuous	grief	nervous	skeptical	
contented	groovy	nutty	sneaky	
contrite	guilty		solemn	
cruel	gullible	obnoxious	sorrowful	
crushed		obsessed	spiteful	
culpable	happy	odd	startled	
	hassled	opposed	stingy	
deceitful	hate	outraged	stuffed	
defeated	heavenly	overwhelmed	stupid	
delighted	helpful		stunned	
desirous	helpless	pain	stupefied	
despairing	high	panicked	suffering	
destructive	homesick	parsimonious	sure	
determined	honored	peaceful	sympathetic	
diffident	hurt	persecuted		
diminished	hysterical	petrified	talkative	
distracted		pity	tempted	

73

References

Bairre, C. (2016, December 6). *Be intentional in all you do!* Live • Love • Work.
    http://chrysta.tribeofdiamonds.com/2013/03/15/be-intentional-in-all-you-do/

Berne, E. (1996). *Games people play: The basic handbook of transactional analysis.* Ballantine.

Bolthouse, E. (2006). Correlation of Grapes and Boundaries. *Boundaries 8-Week Group.*

Buscaglia, L. F., & Kimber, D. (1994). In *Born to love: Reflections on loving.* Fawcett Ballantine.

Calhoun, L., & Tedeschi, R. (2006). Foundations of posttraumatic growth. In L. Calhoun, & R.
    Tedeschi, *Handbook of posttraumatic growth: Research and practice* (pp. 3-23). Lawrence Erlbaum
    Associates.

Calhoun, L., & Tedeschi, R. (2010). *Facilitating posttraumatic growth: A clinician's guide.* Routledge.

Calhoun, L., Cann, A., Tedeschi, R., & McMillan, J. (2000). A correlational test of the relationship
    between posttraumatic growth, religion, and cognitive processing. *Journal of Traumatic Stress,
    13*(3), 521-527. https://doi.org/10.1023/A:1007745627077

Cloud, H., & Townsend, J. (1992). *Boundaries: When to say yes, how to say no to take control of your life.*
    Zondervan.

Crawford, J., Vallance, J., Holt, N., & Courneya, K. (2015). Associations between exercise and
    posttraumatic growth in gynecologic cancer survivors. *Support Care Cancer, 23*, 705-714.
    https://doi.org/10.1007/s00520-014-2410-1

Doka, K. J. (2002). *Disenfranchised grief: New directions, challenges and strategies for practice.* Research Press.

Doka, K. J. (2018). Growth in grief: A historical perspective. In K. J. Doka & A. S. Tucci (Eds.)
    Transforming loss: Finding potential for growth (pp. 5-17). Hospice Foundation of America.

Doran, G. (1981). There's a S.M.A.R.T. way to write management's goals and objectives. *Management
    Review. AMA FORUM 70*(11), 35-36.

Engelkemeyer, S., & Marwit, S. (2008). Posttraumatic growth in bereaved parents. *Journal of Traumatic
    Stress, 21*(3), 344-346. https://doi.org/10.1002/jts.20338

Green, B., Krupnick, J., Stockton, P., Goodman, L., Corcoran, C., & Petty, R. (2001, January).
    Psychological outcomes associated with traumatic loss in a sample of young women. *American
    Behavioral Scientist, 44*(5), 817-837. https://doi.org/10.1177/00027640121956511

Hagenaars, M., & van Minnen, A. (2010, August). Posttraumatic growth in exposure therapy for PTSD.
    Journal of Traumatic Stress, 23(4), 504-508. https://doi.org/10.1002/jts.20551

Harbin, A. (2015). Prescribing posttraumatic growth. *Bioethics, 29*(9), 671-679.
    https://doi.org/10.1111/bioe.12164

Harris, D., & Winokuer, H. (2016). *Principles and practice of grief counseling.* Springer Publishing.

Hoge, E., Austin, E., & Pollack, M. (2007). Resilience: Research evidence and conceptual considerations for posttraumatic stress disorder. *Depression and Anxiety, 24*(2), 139-152. https://doi.org/10.1002/da.20175

Jung, C. G. (1971). Chapter X. In *The collected works of C.G. Jung* (Vol. 6). (2nd ed.). Princeton University Press.

Kilmer, R., Gil-Rivas, V., Tedeschi, R., Cann, A., Calhoun, L., Buchanan, T., & Taku, K. (2009, June). Use of the revised posttraumatic growth inventory for children. *Journal of Traumatic Stress, 22*(3), 248-253. https://doi.org/10.1002/jts.20410

Kunst, M. (2010). Peritraumatic distress, posttraumatic stress disorder symptoms, and posttraumatic growth in victims of violence. *Journal of Traumatic Stress, 23*(4), 514-518. https://doi.org/10.1002/jts.20556

LaMorie, J. (2013, March 21). *Recognizing and grieving secondary losses.* Tragedy Assistance Program for Survivors, Inc. (TAPS): https://www.taps.org/articles/19-1/secondaryloss.

Lepore, S., & Revenson, T. (2006). Resilience and posttraumatic growth, recovery, resistance, and reconfiguration. In L. Calhoun, & R. Tedeschi (Eds.), *Handbook of Posttraumatic Growth* (pp. 24-46). Lawrence Erlbaum Associates Publishers.

Litz, B., Orsillo, S., Kaloupek, D., & Weathers, F. (2000, February). Emotional processing in posttraumatic stress disorder. *Journal of Abnormal Psychology, 109*(1), 26-39. https://doi.org/10.1037/0021-843X.109.1.26

Mancini, A., Robinaugh, D., Shear, K., & Bonanno, G. (2009, October). Does attachment avoidance help people cope with loss? The moderating effects of relationship quality. *Journal of Clinical Psychology, 65*(10), 1127-1136. https://doi.org/10.1002/jclp.20601

Miller, D. (2010). *48 days to the work you love: Preparing for the new normal.* Broadman & Holman.

Mols, F., Vingerhoets, J., Coebergh, J., & van d Poll-Franse, L. (2009, June). Well-being, posttraumatic growth and benefit finding in long-term breast cancer survivors. *Psychology and Health, 24*(5), 583-595. https://doi.org/10.1080/08870440701671362

Murphy, S., Johnson, L., Chung, I., & Beaton, R. (2003). The prevalence of PTSD following the violent death of a child and predictors of change 5 years later. *Journal of Traumatic Stress, 16*(1), 17-25. https://doi.org/10.1023/A:1022003126168

Neria, Y., & Litz, B. (2004, January 1). Bereavement by traumatic means: The complex synergy of trauma and grief. *Journal of Loss and Trauma, 9*(1), 73-87. https://doi.org/10.1080/15325020490255322

Proffitt, D., Cann, A., Calhoun, L., & Tedeschi, R. (2007, June). Judeo-Christian clergy and personal crisis: Religion, posttraumatic growth and well being. *Journal of Religio and Health, 46*(2), 219-231. https://doi.org/10.1007/s10943-006-9074-1

Sandler, I., Wolchik, S., & Ayers, T. (2008). Resilience rather than recovery: A contextual framework on adaptation following bereavement. *Death Studies, 32*(1), 59-73. https://doi.org/10.1080/07481180701741343

Schwartz, A. (2020). The post-traumatic growth guidebook: Practical mind-body tools to heal trauma, foster resilience and awaken your potential. PESI Publishing.

Shakespeare-Finch, J., & Enders, T. (2008, August). Corroborating evidence of posttraumatic growth. *Journal of Traumatic Stress, 21*(4), 421-424. https://doi.org/10.1002/jts.20347

Shear, M.K. (2015). Complicated grief treatment (CGT) for prolonged grief disorder. In U. Schnyder, & M. Cloitre, Evidence based treatments for trauma-related psychological disorders: A practical guide for clinicians (pp. 299-314). Springer Publishing.

Shear, M., Simon, N., Wall, M., Zisook, S., & Niemeyer, R. (2011). Complicated grief and related bereavement issues for DSM-5. Depression and Anxiety, 28(2), 103-117. https://doi.org/10.1002/da.20780

Silverstein, M., Witte, T., Lee, D., Kramer, L., & Weathers, F. (2018, June). Dimensions of growth? Examining the distinctiveness of the five factors of the posttraumatic growth inventory. Journal of Traumatic Stress, 31(3), 448-453. https://doi.org/10.1002/jts.22298

Solomon, C. (2003, January). Transactional analysis theory: The basics. Transactional Analysis Journal, 33(1), 15-22. https://doi.org/10.1177/036215370303300103

Tedeschi, R., & Calhoun, L. (1995). Trauma & transformation: Growing in the aftermath of suffering. Sage Publications.

Tedeschi, R., & Calhoun, L. (1996). The Posttraumatic Growth Inventory: Measuring the positive legacy of trauma. Journal of Traumatic Stress, 9, 455-472. https://doi.org/10.1002/jts.2490090305

Tedeschi, R., & Calhoun, L. (2004). Posttraumatic growth: Conceptual foundations and empirical evidence. Psychological Inquiry 15(1), 1-18. https://doi.org/10.1207/s15327965pli1501_01

Tedeschi, R., & Moore, B. (2016). The Posttraumatic Growth Workbook: Coming Through Trauma Wiser, Stronger, and More Resilient. New Harbinger.

Tedeschi, R., Cann, A., Taku, K., Senol-Durak, E., & Calhoun, L. (2017, February). The posttraumatic growth inventory: A revision integrating existential and spiritual change. Journal of Traumatic Stress, 30, 11-18. https://doi.org/10.1002/jts.22155

Wilkinson, B. (2001). Secrets of the vine: Breaking through to abundance. Multnomah.

Winokuer, H. & Harris, D. (2012). Principles and practice of grief counseling. Springer Publishing.

Worden, J. (2009). Grief counseling and grief therapy: A handbook for the mental health practitioner. Springer Publishing.